Happily
Ever After

>>》》》×《《《《‹

The Little Mermaid

First published in the UK in 2018
by New Frontier Publishing Europe Pty
93 Harbord Street, London SW6 6PN
www.newfrontierpublishing.co.uk

ISBN: 978-1-912076-90-1 (PB)

A CIP catalogue record for this book is available from
the British Library.

Printed in China
10 9 8 7 6 5 4 3 2 1

Happily Ever After

The Little Mermaid

Illustrated by Owen Swan

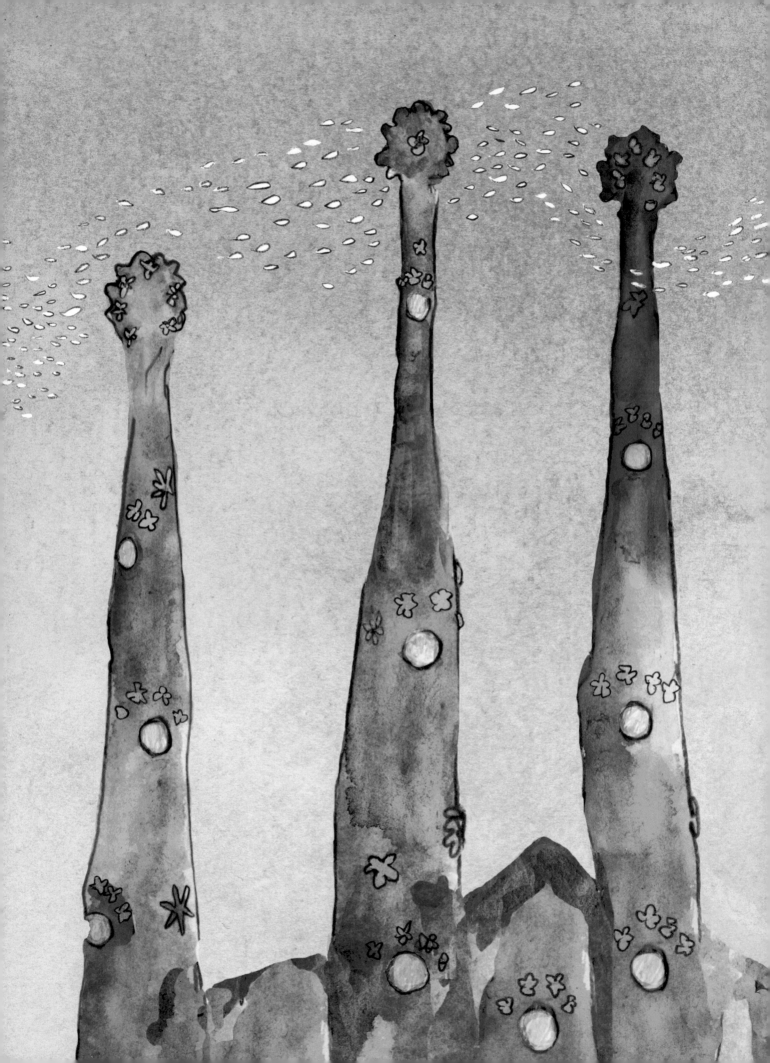

Deep down at the bottom of the ocean stood the Sea King's great palace. Its walls were built from coral and its roof from shells.

The King had six daughters who lived under the sea. They all enjoyed diving down to collect treasure from ships – except for Ariel, the youngest, who dreamed only of flowers and sunshine.

Young mermaids could only live underwater,
but when they turned fifteen they were
allowed to visit the surface of the ocean to
look at the passing ships.

Every year Ariel's sisters came back with news of what they had seen – the ships, the green ocean and the icebergs. But after a while the girls got tired of life above the water. It was much prettier down below at the bottom of the ocean, in their father's palace.

Sometimes they went up to the surface and sang to the ships. Humans had never heard such sweet voices.

At last it was Ariel's turn. When she lifted her head above the water for the first time, she saw a magnificent ship. Inside was a handsome prince who was celebrating his sixteenth birthday. Fireworks lit up the sky as the sailors joined in the celebrations. Ariel couldn't take her eyes off the prince.

But a dark storm was brewing. It struck the ship and broke it into pieces. Ariel searched for the prince and found him struggling to swim to shore. She remembered that humans can't survive at the bottom of the ocean and held his head above the water. She sang to him on the sandy shore, hoping he would soon wake.

The next morning a young girl found the prince on the shore. Ariel tried to walk over to them but her fish tail would only let her swim in the water.

Ariel swam back down
to her home. One of
her sisters found out
where the prince lived
and took Ariel to see his
palace from the water.

The next day Ariel went to visit the Sea Witch
to ask for legs so she could be with the prince.
In exchange for the potion the Sea Witch asked
for Ariel's voice. Ariel agreed.

She went up to the surface of the ocean and
drank the potion.

When she woke, she had two legs instead
of a tail.

But she could not speak or sing to the prince
because the Sea Witch had taken
her voice.

The prince's father told the prince that he had to marry and took him to see a princess in a nearby town.

On the day of the prince's wedding Ariel was sad.

She couldn't be with the prince, and she couldn't go back to her family at the bottom of the ocean.

The Sea King rose up from the depths of the ocean and ordered the Sea Witch to give Ariel back her voice.

Ariel began singing and the prince recognised her voice straightaway as the voice of the mermaid who had saved him.

He walked out of the palace to the edge of
the ocean where Ariel was waiting for him and
they lived happily ever after.